Usborne English Readers

Level 2

The Phantom of the Opera

Retold by Mairi Mackinnon
Illustrated by Elena Selivanova

English language consultant: Peter Viney

Contents

You can listen to the story online here:
www.usborneenglishreaders.com/
phantomoftheopera

It was early evening in the Paris Opera House. The singers and musicians were almost ready for the performance. Carlotta, the famous soprano, was sitting in her dressing room. The room was full of flowers, but Carlotta didn't even notice them. She was worried about her voice. She needed to sing well tonight.

Somebody knocked at the door. "Go away!" croaked Carlotta. What was wrong with her voice? The door opened anyway, and five or six young singers hurried into the room. Their faces were white and frightened.

"What happened?" asked Carlotta. "Have you seen a ghost?"

"*Yes!*" said one. "It was the Phantom!"

"We all saw him," said another. "He's so tall, so thin!"

"He always wears evening clothes, and a cloak."

"Ha! So do hundreds of people at the opera every night," said Carlotta.

"Yes, but he also wears a mask! They say he is horribly ugly, under that mask."

"And I suppose he never speaks, this phantom," said Carlotta.

"Almost never – but tonight he spoke," said the youngest singer. "He said, 'Tell Carlotta she sings like a toad, and I never want to hear her voice again.'"

Carlotta was very angry. She opened her mouth, but no sound came out – nothing at all. Her voice was gone!

"But it's only an hour until the performance!" said Monsieur Richard, the new manager. "Carlotta is our Marguerite! Who else can sing that part? It's impossible!"

"Christine can," said one of the young singers. "I've heard her in her dressing room. Her voice is much better than anyone thinks. I've heard her singing Marguerite."

"Who is her teacher?" asked Monsieur Richard.

"Nobody knows. She says she has an Angel of Music."

"Huh!" said Monsieur Richard – but he still asked to see Christine.

The opera house was full that evening. Before the performance, Monsieur Richard came on to the stage and spoke to the audience. "I'm afraid Carlotta is ill. Christine will sing the part of Marguerite instead." That surprised everybody.

"Who is this Christine?"

"She's very young, isn't she – and it's such an important part."

"What is this manager doing?"

The first half of the opera went well. Then it was time for Christine's solo, and this was the biggest surprise of all. Her voice was wonderful, and she sang the part perfectly.

At the end, everyone in the audience stood up and cheered loudly.

After the performance, one young man hurried to the stage door. "I need to see Christine. I'm an old friend."

"Christine is very tired, sir."

"Please – I know she'll see me." He soon found Christine's room. The young singer looked up and smiled. "Raoul! You're here! How wonderful."

"Christine, you were amazing. I hope you sing the part every night."

"You're very kind," said Christine, "but I don't think I can sing it again. I'm sorry, Raoul – I need to rest now." She closed her eyes, and he left the room.

Suddenly he heard a man's voice. "That's not possible," thought Raoul. "There was nobody else there." But a man was speaking, and Christine was answering.

Then the door opened and Christine came out. She didn't notice Raoul. He waited a moment and then opened the door, but the room was completely empty.

M onsieur Richard was reading a letter.

That's enough – no more Carlotta. I want to hear Christine every night. You must keep the best seat in the house for me.

Also, the old manager paid me 20,000 francs every month. You must do the same.

The Phantom

"Twenty thousand francs? Certainly not!" shouted the manager. "And I'm not going to keep an empty seat for a ghost. I don't believe in ghosts. I don't care if the old manager paid a million francs or more. Carlotta will sing again as soon as her voice is better."

Raoul was following Christine through the streets. He had so many questions! Christine walked quickly, and soon they were far away from the opera house. They came to some old metal gates. Christine went through the gates, and hurried across to a simple gravestone.

"Dear Father," she said. "I know you can hear me. Oh, what should I do? I'm so happy... and so frightened... and I think I'm in love."

In love! What did she mean?

Suddenly Raoul heard music – the most beautiful violin music. Christine's father was a violinist, he remembered – but the old man never played like this.

"My Angel of Music!" said Christine.

Then Raoul saw the violinist. He was standing near the gravestone. He was a tall, thin man in a long cloak, and he had a mask on his face. "Christine, be careful!" Raoul shouted. The other man stepped forward, and Raoul saw two terrible red eyes behind the mask. Christine screamed, "Don't hurt him!" Raoul fell back, and everything went dark.

Raoul woke in his own home. He didn't remember coming back there, but he felt much better. Then he saw a letter from Christine.

My dear Raoul,

I hope you were not hurt last night. Please forget everything you saw. I love you, and I want you to be safe. Please don't try to find my Angel of Music. Everyone thinks he's a monster, but he has been very good to me.

Your

Christine

In another home across the city, Carlotta was also reading a letter.

Do not try to sing again. If you do, something terrible will happen.

The Phantom

"Who is this?" said Carlotta. "The Phantom? I don't believe it. It must be Christine, or one of her friends. I'm not frightened of them!"

The opera house was full again that evening. "Is Christine singing tonight?" people asked. "No, it's Carlotta."

"That's a pity." Raoul agreed, but he waited with everyone else for Carlotta's solo. The musicians started playing. Carlotta came to the front of the stage and opened her mouth...

"CRO-AK!"

"She sounds like a toad!"

Carlotta tried not to hear. She opened her mouth again. "CRO-AK!" People started to laugh.

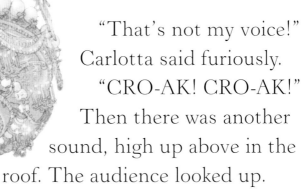

"That's not my voice!" Carlotta said furiously.

"CRO-AK! CRO-AK!" Then there was another sound, high up above in the roof. The audience looked up.

The enormous chandelier was moving from side to side. The people in the seats below stood up and ran, just before the chandelier fell to the ground. Then all the lights went out, and there was a horrible laugh.

"It's the Phantom!" someone screamed. The lights came on again, and everyone ran towards the doors.

Where are my 20,000 francs?
When will Christine sing again?
I am waiting...

The Phantom

Monsieur Richard threw the letter across the room. "*Your* twenty thousand francs?" he shouted. "It's costing millions of francs to repair the roof and the chandelier. We've had no performances for a week. There is no money, Phantom!" Then he said, "What am I doing? Talking to myself? There is no phantom. *I don't believe in ghosts.*"

Raoul was visiting Christine. "Please, don't go back to the opera house," he said. "Your Angel of Music – the Phantom – is dangerous. You don't have to sing again. Christine, please marry me. We can go far away from Paris, and be happy together."

Christine looked at him. "I'm sorry, Raoul. I love you, but I'm so frightened. If I marry you, what will he do? The opera house opens again tomorrow. They have asked me to sing, and I will. Don't worry, my love."

The opera house was not so full that night. After the accident with the chandelier, people were very frightened, but many still wanted to hear Christine. Raoul looked around. He could see policemen by some of the doors.

Christine began to sing. Her voice was more beautiful than ever, and the audience cheered and cheered. Suddenly the lights went out, and there was a scream. When the lights came on again, Christine was gone.

Raoul ran up to the stage. The police were behind him. "Where is she? Doesn't anybody know anything?"

"She just disappeared, from the middle of the stage! No one has seen her anywhere." The police searched the stage and all the dressing rooms. Of course Christine's dressing room was empty, but Raoul stayed there for a moment and looked around.

"That night, when I heard a man's voice," he thought. "I wonder..?"

He started pushing at the walls. Suddenly a part of the wall moved, and Raoul was looking into the dark behind it.

"Police! Follow me," he shouted. "Bring a light!"

Lights appeared behind him. "I am Inspector Faure. I'm coming with you," said a strong voice. "I'm bringing four of my men."

Raoul stepped into a narrow passage. "The Phantom is somewhere in here, I'm sure," he said. He and the policemen hurried further and further along the passage.

Suddenly it opened up ahead of them, and the lights were reflecting on...

"Water!" said Raoul. "It's an underground lake!"

"I've heard about this," said the inspector. "It's been here ever since they built the place."

"Look, there's a boat," said Raoul. "Let's cross the lake."

"Are you sure?" asked the inspector. Then, from far away, they heard a woman's voice. "Help me..."

"That's Christine!" said Raoul. "We must hurry." He and the inspector jumped into the boat. Soon they were on the other side, and they could see lights ahead. Raoul ran towards them. He could see trees and flowers too. How was that possible?

Then the lights were very bright, and the trees were all around him. Suddenly a door closed. "It's a trick! We can't get out," said the inspector.

Raoul looked at the trees. He could see now that they weren't real. Their flowers were made of paper. "It's a room made of mirrors. The mirrors reflect the trees and the lights all around us."

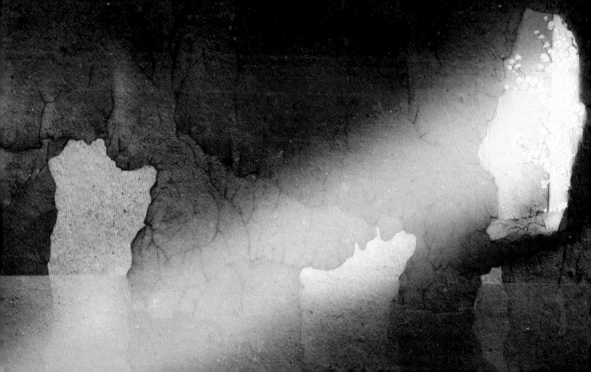

"Raoul, Raoul, be brave," said Christine's voice above them.

"Christine, where are you?" Raoul searched the room, but he could only see more trees and mirrors, more Raouls and inspectors. "Where is the door? Inspector, we must find it."

"She's very near you now," said a man's voice, "but you can't see her, and you never will. You'll never leave that room."

"You monster!" shouted Raoul.

"Shhh, my love," said Christine. Then her voice changed. "My angel, please, open the door. Those men won't hurt you. Let them go."

"You love him," said the Phantom's voice. "You love him more than you love me."

"It's different!" said Christine. "Please, don't be jealous. You have been so kind to me. You're my good friend."

"You want to marry him, more than you want to marry me. Will you marry me?"

"I –" began Christine.

"Stop!" shouted Raoul. He and the inspector pushed at the mirrors and tried to break them, but they couldn't. The room was warmer now. There wasn't enough air.

"I told you, you will never leave that room," said the Phantom's voice. "Now, Christine, say you'll marry me. If you say yes, your friend will live. If you say no..."

"Don't say anything!" shouted Raoul.

"My men are coming," said the inspector. "They will rescue you."

Christine spoke clearly. "I will marry you, my Angel of Music."

"You love this man so much?" The Phantom's voice was quiet. "So much that you will marry a... a monster like me?"

"You're not a monster," said Christine. "Take off your mask."

"The door! It's open," shouted the inspector. He and Raoul hurried out. They could see some stairs now beside the mirror room. At the top of the stairs was another room, an ordinary sitting room with tables and chairs and lights and pictures. There were pages of music everywhere, and a violin in one corner.

"Shh!" said Christine. She was sitting in a chair in the middle of the room. The Phantom was sitting on the floor beside her. He wasn't wearing his mask.

Christine put her hand on his head. "You poor man," she said. "Your life has been very terrible, hasn't it? What is your real name?"

"I am Erik," said the Phantom. He was crying. "You saw my face. You touched me. You asked my name. Even my own mother couldn't look at me. You are the true angel, Christine. Be happy with your young man." He closed his eyes, and put his hand on his heart. "I am dying, Christine. Goodbye."

They heard the sound of heavy feet. "Inspector! Monsieur Raoul! Are you there?" The policemen came into the room. "What is this place? And is that...?"

"His name is Erik," said Christine. "No – his name *was* Erik. He was a wonderful musician, and a very unhappy man. Let him rest now."

For weeks, the newspapers were full of stories about the "real" Phantom and his home by the underground lake.

The stories said that when he was a child, his family sold him to a circus, and people paid to look at his terrible face. Nobody noticed that he was a clever boy, with a beautiful singing voice, and he learned all kinds of tricks from the circus people. He even learned how to change his voice, so that it seemed to come from somewhere else. (He played that trick on poor Carlotta.)

At last he escaped from the circus and became a musician. He lived in different countries around the world, and always hid his face behind a mask. He helped to build the opera house, and nobody ever found out about the secret rooms below.

Then the stories started – the little accidents, the strange man in the cloak and mask – the Phantom of the Opera.

From their new home in the country, Raoul and Christine read the stories and smiled. "Do you miss the Opera, my love?" asked Raoul.

"Not at all!" laughed Christine. "I loved singing, but I never wanted to be on the stage. And Erik frightened me at the end, poor man. Now I sing because I am happy, and I will be happy with you forever."

"Thank you, Erik," said Raoul quietly. "Now at last you can rest."

About the story

Gaston Leroux was a French writer and journalist. He wrote about opera for a Paris newspaper. He also wrote stories for the newspapers. They were serials, with an exciting new part every week or even every day. In 1909-1910, *The Phantom of the Opera* was one of these stories.

Leroux knew the Paris Opera House, which is now called the Opéra Garnier, very well. He knew that there really is water under the Opera House, from an underground river (not a lake). There are even fish in it. Then Leroux had the idea of someone secretly living under the building...

In 1926, *The Phantom of the Opera* became a popular silent film. There have been many more film versions over the years, as well as a famous musical. Over 140 million people in 35 countries have seen the musical.

Activities

The answers are on page 40.

Mixed-up story

Can you put these pictures and sentences in order?

A.

"I love you, but I'm so frightened."

B.

"My Angel of Music!" she said.

C.

"I will be happy with you forever."

D.

Christine was gone.

E.

At the end, everyone cheered loudly.

F.

"You poor man," she said.

Who's who?

Choose two sentences for each person.

Carlotta   Monsieur Richard   Christine

A.
He is the
new opera
manager.

B.
She is very
young.

C.
He is an old
friend of
Christine's.

G.
He follows
Raoul to
the lake.

H.
He is a
wonderful
musician.

I.
He doesn't
believe in
ghosts.

Raoul   The Phantom   Inspector Faure

D.
He lives by an
underground
lake.

E.
She is a
famous
soprano.

F.
He asks Christine
to go away from
Paris with him.

J.
She loses
her voice.

K.
She is
frightened of
the Phantom.

L.
He says his
men will rescue
Christine.

The Phantom's letters

Choose a word to finish each letter.

1.

I want to ....
Christine every night.

follow   hear   recognize

2.

You must .... the
best seat for me.

hide   keep   share

3.

Do not try to
.... again.

fight   rest   sing

4.

I am ....

calling   explaining   waiting

Which is true?

Choose the right sentence for each picture.

1.

A. Carlotta was worried about her voice.

B. Carlotta was happy about her voice.

2.

A. Raoul saw a man talking.

B. Raoul heard a man talking.

3.

A. Raoul felt terrible.

B. Raoul felt much better.

4.

A. Raoul searched the room.

B. Raoul smelled the flowers.

Word list

angel (n) people believe that angels are good and powerful and live in heaven.

audience (n) the people who come to see a play or a film, or to hear a concert (music).

chandelier (n) a chandelier hangs from the ceiling of a room and has lots of candles or electric lights. It is usually made of glass and metal.

cheer (v) when you cheer, you shout to show that you think something is really good.

circus (n) a group of performers, for example acrobats and clowns, who travel from place to place. In the past, some circuses had lions, elephants and other animals. Long ago, they sometimes included people with strange faces or bodies.

cloak (n) a type of large, loose coat without sleeves.

croak (n, excl, v) the noise that a frog or toad makes.

dressing room (n) the room where an actor, a singer or dancer gets ready before a performance.

franc (n) the old type of money used in France, before euros.

ghost (n) some people believe that when a person dies, they can become a ghost. In stories, ghosts are usually unhappy or frightening.

gravestone (n) the special stone used to mark the place where a dead person is buried.

inspector (n) a senior policeman.

manager (n) an important person in a company or organisation. A manager makes decisions about what a company does, who works for it and how to spend the company's money.

mask (n) you wear a mask to hide your face. People sometimes wear masks in plays or at parties.

mirror (n) a mirror is made of glass and metal. People use mirrors to see what they look like.

Monsieur (n) the French word for Mr.

opera (n) in a play, actors speak the parts. In an opera, singers sing them, with an orchestra.

passage (n) a narrow way between rooms or between parts of a building.

performance (n) a piece of music, acting or dance for an audience.

phantom (n) another word for ghost.

reflect (v) to show the exact image of something. Mirrors reflect, and metal or water can also reflect things.

repair (v) to fix something that is broken.

search (v) to look very carefully for someone or something.

seat (n) the place where you sit, especially for a performance or in a car, train or plane.

solo (n) a piece of music or dance for just one performer.

soprano (n) a woman with a high singing voice, especially in classical music.

stage (n) the place where the main action happens in plays and operas.

step (v) when you move forward and start to walk, you step.

toad (n) a small animal like a frog. Most people think toads are ugly and not very nice.

violin (n) a musical instrument with four strings.

Answers

Mixed-up story
E, B, A, D, F, C

Who's who?
Carlotta – E, J
Monsieur Richard – A, I
Christine – B, K
Raoul – C, F
The Phantom – D, H
Inspector Faure – G, L

The Phantom's letters
1. hear
2. keep
3. sing
4. waiting

Which is true?
1. A
2. B
3. B
4. A

You can find information about other Usborne English Readers here: www.usborneenglishreaders.com

Designed by Sam Whibley
Series designer: Laura Nelson Norris
Edited by Jane Chisholm
With thanks to Andy Prentice
Digital imaging: Nick Wakeford

Page 32: picture of Gaston Leroux © Granger, NYC/TopFoto.

First published in 2018 by Usborne Publishing Ltd.,
Usborne House, 83-85 Saffron Hill, London EC1N 8RT, England.
www.usborne.com Copyright © 2018 Usborne Publishing Ltd.